Not For SNOWFLAKES

An Atheist's Missal – with Jokes

Johnnie Fraser

Published by John Fraser 2019

Copyright © 2019

First edition.

ISBN:
978-1-5272-5498-5 - paperback

If Liberty means anything at all, it means the right to tell people what they do not want to hear.
George Orwell

It is only by hearing manifold informed opinions on every subject under the sun – on death, religion, politics, morality – no matter how much we might disagree, it is only by listening to views contrary to our own that we can begin to approach Wisdom.
J.F.

It is ironic that University students, regarded as the cream of our intelligent youth, refuse to allow anyone to address them whose views they don't share. The time honoured and tested method devised by Socrates to get to the truth – 'Adversarial Debate' – is being stifled by Political Correctness.
J.F.

The World is my country, all mankind are my brethren, and to do good is my religion.
Thomas Paine

Faith is believin' what you know ain't so.
Mark Twain

I've no interest in religion. I've tried, but I start laughing.
Bob Hoskins

We must respect the other fellow's religion, but only in the sense and to the extent that we respect his theory that his wife is beautiful and his children smart.
H. L. Mencken

Faith does not give you the answers; it just stops you asking the questions.
Frater Ravus

Facts do not cease to exist because they are ignored.
Aldous Huxley

Faith means not wanting to know what is true.
Friedrich Nietzsche

Free will is a fiction worth maintaining.
Sam Harris

When I was a kid I used to pray every night for a new bicycle. Then I realised that the Lord doesn't work that way so I stole one and asked Him to forgive me.
Emo Philips

George Bush says he speaks to God every day, and Christians love him for it. If George Bush said he spoke to God through his hair dryer, they would think he was mad. I fail to see how the addition of a hair dryer makes it any more absurd.
George Carlin.

Religion has actually convinced people that there's an invisible man living in the sky who watches everything you do, every minute of every day. And the invisible man has a special list of ten things he does not want you to do and if you do any of these ten things, he has a special place, full of fire and smoke and burning and torture and anguish, where he will send you to live and suffer and burn and choke and scream and cry forever and ever till the end of time! But He loves you.
Delos B. McKown

People who don't like their beliefs being laughed at shouldn't have such funny beliefs.
Friedrich Nietzsche

The presence of those seeking the truth is infinitely to be preferred to the presence of those who think they've found it. Maybe we can't convince people that religion is evil (and not *all* are, viz Quakers), but I think religion would be better if we left out the goddy parts. Then it wouldn't be religion anymore, but secular humanism.

FOMO
Fear of missing out.
What is wanted is not the will to believe, but the will to find out, which is its exact opposite.
Bertrand Russell

I believe that when I die I shall rot and that nothing of my ego will survive. I am an old man, but I scorn to fear annihilation, and still believe in love and the pursuit of understanding even although they are finite.
Bertrand Russell

Nothing is as difficult as not deceiving yourself.
Ludwig Wittgenstein.

With or without religion, you would have good people doing good things and evil people doing evil things, but for good people to do evil things, that takes religion.
Steven Weinberg

Suicide Bombers:-
Man's basest instincts need the sanction of his highest to wreak the most havoc.
J.F.

Language is a cracked kettle on which we beat out tunes for bears to dance to, while all the time we long to move the stars to pity.
Flaubert, **Madame Bovary**

The mind is the activity of an organ that runs by physiological processes. There are methods of ascertaining the truth that can force us to conclusions which violate common sense, sometimes radically so at scales very large and very small. Precious and widely held beliefs when subjected to empirical tests are often cruelly falsified.
Steven Pinker

The human brain is capable of such lofty and astonishing things that their expression has been given the names *imagination* and *soul* and *spirit*.
Marilynne Robinson

He: Will you sleep with me for a million dollars?
She: I'll have to think about it.
He: Will you sleep with me for a hundred dollars
She: What kind of woman do you take me for?
He: We've already established that. We're just haggling over the price.

We meet our destiny on the road we take to avoid it.
Carl Jung

Sapere aude
Dare to know.
Immanuel Kant.

Titans
Nelson Mandela, Ayaan Hirsi Ali, David Attenborough,
Steven Pinker, Alice Hertz-Sommers, Christiane Amanpour,
Helen Suzman, Jane Fonda, Sam Harris, Bill Maher, Jon
Snow,Brian Cox (Astronomer), Brian Cox (Actor **and my
cherished friend.**) John Carey, Judi Dench, Barack and
Michelle Obama, Matt Damon, Richard Dawkins, Billy
Connolly, Majid Nawaz, Ed Husain.

Who is she that looketh forth as the morning, fair as the
moon, clear as the sun, and terrible as an army with banners.
Song of Solomon.

(Tommy) about the hypocritical Left:
They mock the uniforms of those who guard their sleep.
Rudyard Kipling

Near this spot are deposited the remains of one who possessed
beauty without vanity, strength without insolence, courage
without ferocity, and all the virtues of man without his vices.
Lord Byron (on his dog's tombstone.)

No memory of having starred
Atones for later disregard
Or keeps the end from being hard.
Robert Frost

Happiness makes up in height for what it lacks in length. The ingredients essential to happiness are love and friendship.
J.F.

Seeking the bubble reputation even in the cannon's mouth. –
As You Like It

God can only be present in creation under the form of absence. !!!!!!!!!!!!!!
Simone Weil

God is by definition, that reality which makes a total difference to the way we perceive ourselves. !!!!!!!!!!!!!!!!!!!!
Richard Harries, Bishop of Oxford.

Bacteria swim towards sugar and away from acid.
John Gray, *Straw Dogs*

A claim to knowledge has to be substantiated.
Ignorance need only be confessed.
Anthony Kenny

The difference between an Italian Mamma and a Jewish Mamma. To her little boy, at the table:
Italian Mamma: "If you don't eat your dinner, I'll kill you!"
Jewish Mamma: "If you don't eat your dinner, I'll kill myself!"

If you have to belong to a minority, it's better to be black than gay. When you're black, you don't have to tell your mother.

A Scotsman: He loved his wife so much he nearly told her.
Billy Connolly

Pitfalls for translators: In Paris. A cowboy film subtitled in
French. John Wayne enters a bar:- "Gimme a shot of Red
Eye." Subtitle. "Un Dubonnet, s'il vous plait."

Science has shown that it is not witchcraft which causes
disease, but bacteria.

A two-line poem on a scrap of lined paper in a child's writing
found under a bunk in Auschwitz.
"Who will hold your hand when you are dying?
Who will close your eyes after you are dead?"

W. H. Auden (On Death.)

Distant thunder at a picnic.
I'll love you till Africa and India meet
Till streams leap over the mountain
And the salmon sing in the street.

Kubla Khan attempting to seize Japan. Flat bottomed gun
boats on the sea-bed and a wind from heaven. Thousands
of warships, men and warhorses in elaborate armour at the
bottom of the sea rusting in a forest of weed.

Three may keep a secret if two of them are dead.

Cowards in scarlet pass for men of war.

Christianity has a five-hundred-year start on Islam.
"That means we'll have to wait five hundred years for some
good Mohammed jokes."
"Osama bin Laden shows all the symptoms of the fifty-
third son syndrome."
Crispin Cole

Writing a letter to a friend Voltaire apologises for its length. "I had no time to make it shorter."

Un uom senza dinar quanto par brutto.
How ugly a man looks when he has no money.
Antonio Cammelli

My arguments may persuade you, but this will not show that they are true, only that they are persuasive.
We cannot talk of truth and falsehood except where proof is available, and where proof is available, persuasion is not needed.
John Carey, *What Good Are The Arts?*

A kind of immortality:-
In The Royal Geographical Society, a glazed box containing 'Icicle', a stuffed baby penguin. An Arctic expedition found him lost without his mother. On their journey home to London they tried to keep him alive with a diet of sardines and bananas. Without success. So they had him stuffed where he can be admired till he returns to the primordial dust.

A bust of Queen Victoria is set on the windowsill so that she can look on the statue of her adored husband Prince Albert resplendent in gold, on his Memorial across the road in Kensington Gardens. The profound humanity of the RGS is evident in all their endeavours. I am proud to be:- A Fellow!!

Men seek eminence as an end in itself. Women seek many things, and sometimes achieve eminence in consequence.
J.F.

The media are undermined by a "systematic bias in terms of structural economic causes rather than a conspiracy of people." !!!!!!!!!!!!!!!
Noam Chomsky.

If the Lebrovitzes are approaching the Church Universal, that is one thing. But if the Church Universal is approaching the Lebrovitzes, that is quite another matter!!!!!!!!!!!!

Twentieth century parson

If God does not know about evil, he is not omniscient.
If he knows and does nothing, he is malign.
If he does not know and does nothing, why call him God?
Is God willing to prevent evil, but not able?
Then he is impotent. Is he able but not willing?
Then he is malevolent. Is he both able and willing?
Whence then is evil?

Epicurus.

When something is inevitable, embrace it.

Chinese proverb

Her finely-touched spirit had still its fine issues, though they were not widely visible. Her full nature, like that river of which Cyrus broke the strength, spent itself in channels which had no great name on earth. But the effect of her being on those around her was incalculably diffusive: for the growing good of the world is partly dependent on unhistorical acts; and that things are not so ill with you and me as they might have been, is half owing to the number who lived faithfully a hidden life, and rest in unvisited tombs.

George Eliot, last paragraph of *Middlemarch*

Properly read, the Bible is the most potent force for atheism ever conceived.

Isaac Asimov.

Those who can make you believe absurdities can make you commit atrocities.

Voltaire.

It's easier to change the world than to change yourself.
Nelson Mandela

Doubt is not a pleasant condition, but certainty is absurd.
Thomas Paine.

To argue with a man who has renounced his reason is like giving medicine to the dead.
The world holds two classes of men – intelligent men without religion, or religious men without intelligence.
Abdu'l-Ala-A-Ma'arri. Syrian poet, 973–1057

Why be born again when you can grow up?
Anon

***

We rose at 4.30 am to drive to Borobudur, to watch the sun rise over the biggest Buddhist Temple complex in the world, built on the island of Java in Indonesia in the ninth century. The ancient Stupas and the majestic Seated Buddhas black with age and humidity seemed to float on the swirling morning mists that still clung to the dew damp earth; then slowly, slowly a hazy sun trembled awake on the horizon. The tendrils of mist drifting like distant music around the monumental ruins became spun gold, and imperceptibly the Mighty Black Buddhas materialised out of the darkness. The awe inspired by this natural phenomenon is surely the same as that experienced by the religious in a cathedral when they feel close to their God.

The wonderful Rob Edwards was doing *Hamlet*, and I was playing Polonius, Ophelia's well-meaning but meddlesome father. The set which we always carried with us, fitted into three trunks. We piled into our minibus to take us back to the hotel for lunch and a much-needed nap, before our performance in the afternoon in an open pavilion in the *kraton* – the courtyard – of the Sultan's Palace in Yogyaharta. One over-enthusiastic critic's review in Yokohama read "They travel with only three drunks." This raised the audiences' expectations, which I am happy to report were never met.

There were six long poles (which came apart for packing), bearing six masks on top which the cast used when anonymous stage hands were required. They gave the impression of wide-awake watchers to the actions onstage – eavesdropping occurs throughout – "Something is rotten in the state of Denmark."

The poles were hung with a long, regal banner, in scarlet and gold, which could be arranged to define different spaces, and formed a wonderful 'Bear Pit' for the duel between Hamlet and Laertes near the end, Claudius, Gertrude, Ophelia, Horatio and others watching from above.

Halfway through the play Polonius comes to Gertrude's private quarters to warn her of her son's madness. The old man fears that the Prince, in his deranged state, might ravage his daughter Ophelia. While Polonius is talking with the Queen,

Hamlet answers his mother's summons, and Gertrude in a panic begs Polonius to hide behind the *arras* – the regal banner in this case.

During Hamlet's discussion with his mother there is a movement from behind the curtain. Shouting "A rat! A rat!" Hamlet whips out his sword and runs it through the curtain where Polonius is hidden.

The old man falls dying onto the stage, carrying the banner with him. Hamlet cries "Thou wretched, rash intruding fool! I took thee for thy better…" He mistook the eavesdropper for his hated uncle Claudius.

Before this, Polonius (me) has to wait hidden behind the curtain for quite ten minutes awaiting his dramatic entrance, clutching at the Royal Banner while convincingly though not too lingeringly, dying. The play is not called *Polonius* for God's sake, so you have to be quick.

When you're hiding on stage in the murk concentrating on every word and listening for your cue, ten minutes can feel like a long time. As bad luck would have it, that afternoon being particularly torpid and muggy, for the full ten minutes that I was hiding behind 'the arras', I spied an unfamiliar creature far too near my right ear for my peace of mind. I don't like *any* insects in any circumstances or in any climate, but the worst by a long mile are the insects in the tropics. They are first and foremost unfamiliar, weirdly complicated, their feelers thrashing about as if conducting a brisk Viennese waltz, with bulgy eyes…

...and HUGE.

An inadvertent movement behind a curtain…

A skill that many actors worth their salt can accomplish with practice.

In my case I had not even intended to do as the script demanded. It was a reflex over which I had no control. I FLINCHED – vigorously. I flinched as if I were in the throes of an apoplectic seizure.

It is fortuitous that Shakespeare suggests Polonius shouts "Help!" I managed a stifled cry that made no sense, but Rob spitted me on his sword anyway, which was what was required.

What followed when I lay playing dead for an eternity under my 'shroud' was torture worthy of Edgar Allan Poe. A long important, wonderful scene is played between Hamlet and his mother, a scene of love and tragic accusations that would have exploded into farce had Polonius' corpse come to life again. I could feel the bulgy-eyed Huge beastie slithering around my sweat-soaked body seeking an aperture in which to lodge. Had there been even the tiniest zephyr of a tropical breeze to lift the shroud intermittently, the deathly stillness which I had to maintain for *hours* might have been less agonising. "I'll lug the guts into the neighbour room," Hamlet says at last, dragging Polonius off the stage into the heaven of the wings where I could stand up and shake myself like a dog after a swim before plunging into a tepid shower and scrubbing myself all over as if I were infested.

Ophelia tried to comfort me. "It was just a cockroach," she said, smiling sweetly. "Just A Cockroach!!" I yelped. "A Tarantula or a Black Mamba I would have laughed at… but a cockroach… That's the worst thing I can imagine!" Though relatively dry after my shower, in this climate a permanent mist of sweat is irresistible to anything with six legs. I was still scratching and poking in my crevices with the ghastly memory of numberless feet slithering everywhere over my body, a memory that refused, unlike Polonius, to lie down and die.

***

Whatever the natural cause, sin is the true cause
of all earthquakes!!!!!!!
John Wesley

Calling atheism a religion is like calling bald a hair colour.
Dan Hirschberg

Intolerance is the natural concomitant of strong
faith; tolerance grows only when faith loses certainty;
certainty is murderous.
Will Durant

Selective truth is more dangerous than falsehood. The
demonstrably true part gains your trust… but what is left out
can change everything
J.F.

***

More Titans
Descartes, Voltaire, Rousseau. David Hume, Adam
Smith. Jeremy Bentham.

***

Homeopathy. A prolonged and sympathetic consultation with
a patient about his ailments, which is normal in the practise
of homeopathy (and not in traditional medicine), may be
beneficial, but there is no evidence that the therapy produces
better results than a placebo.

Religion rouses ungovernable passions because believers are
aware at subconscious level that their claims are fairy tales. In
argument, the devout's rejection of reason is exposed, bringing
obloquy upon them from people less credulous than they are.

***

RELIGION
Courtesy of RICHARD DAWKINS

To his ten-year-old daughter:

How do we know that the stars, which look like tiny pinpricks in the sky, are really huge balls of fire like the Sun and very far away? The answer is 'evidence'.

Evidence is a good reason for believing something. But I must warn you against three bad reasons for believing anything. They are **'Tradition', 'Authority', and 'Revelation'**.

First**, Tradition**.

A few months ago, I went on television to have a discussion with about fifty children. They were invited because they'd been brought up in lots of different religions. Christians, Jews, Muslims, Hindus, Sikhs.

Their beliefs turned out to have no connection with evidence.

Since they all believed different things they couldn't all be right. Their beliefs all came from tradition. No matter how long ago a story was made up, it is still exactly as true or untrue as the original story was. But why is tradition so important?

You speak English but your friend Erika speaks German. Language is passed down by tradition. There is no other way. In England, Flash is 'a dog'. To Erika he is 'ein Hund'. Neither of these words is more correct, or truer than the other. Both are simply handed down.

Children have to learn the language of their own country, and lots of other things about their own people; and this means that they have to absorb like blotting paper an enormous amount of traditional information. Remember that traditional information just means things that are handed down from grandparents to parents to children. The child's brain has to be a sucker for traditional information. And the child can't be expected to sort out good and useful traditional information, like the words of a language, from bad or silly traditional information, like believing in witches and devils.

Because children have to be suckers for traditional information they are likely to believe anything the grownups tell them.

Lots of what grownups tell them is true and based on evidence or at least sensible. But if some of it is false, silly or even wicked, there is nothing to stop the children believing that too.

When the children grow up they tell it to the next generation of children. So once something gets itself strongly believed – even if it's completely untrue and there never was any reason to believe it in the first place – it can go on forever.

Could this be what happened with religions? Belief that there is a god or gods, belief in Heaven, belief that Mohammed went up to heaven on a winged horse, belief that Jesus never had a human father, belief that prayers are answered, belief that wine turns into blood – not one of these beliefs is backed up by any good evidence. Yet millions of people believe them. Perhaps this is because they were told to believe them when they were young enough to believe anything.

Millions of other people believe quite different things, because they were told different things when they were children. Muslim children are told different things from Christian children, and both grow up utterly convinced that they are right and the others are wrong. Even within Christians, Roman Catholics believe different things from Church of England people or Episcopalians, Shakers or Quakers, Mormons or Holy Rollers, and all are utterly convinced that they are right and the others are wrong. They believe different things for exactly the same kind of reason as you speak English and someone else speaks German. Both languages are in their own country the right language to speak. But it can't be true that different religions are right in their own countries, because different religions claim that opposite things are true. The two other bad reasons for believing in anything: **Authority** and **Revelation**.

Authority as a reason for believing something, means believing it because you are told to believe it by somebody important. In the Roman Catholic Church, the Pope is the most important person. In the Muslim religion the important people are old men with beards called Ayatollahs. Lots of young Muslims are prepared to commit murder, purely because the Ayatollahs in a faraway country tell them to. The present Pope has ordered his followers not to limit the number of babies they have. If people follow his authority as slavishly as he would wish, the results could be terrible famines, diseases and wars, caused by overcrowding.

The third kind of bad reason for believing anything is called '**Revelation**'.

When religious people just have a feeling inside themselves that something must be true, even though there is no evidence that it is true, they call their feeling 'revelation'.

What can we do about all this?

Next time somebody tells you something that sounds important, think to yourself: 'Is this the kind of thing that people probably know because of evidence?"

And, next time somebody tells you that something is true, ask them 'What kind of evidence is there for that?' And if they can't give you a good answer, I hope you'll think very carefully before you believe a word they say.

***

When all you have is a hammer, everything looks like a nail.
Abraham Maslow

How, with this rage, shall beauty hold a plea,
Whose action is no stronger than a flower?
William Shakespeare

We are capable of many things in all directions. Who, in his mind, has not probed the black water?
John Steinbeck.

Sceptical scrutiny is the means, in both science and religion, by which deep insights can be winnowed from deep nonsense.

In science it often happens that scientists say, "You know that's a really good argument; my position is mistaken," and then they would actually change their minds and you never hear that old view from them again. They really do it. It doesn't happen as often as it should, because scientists are human and change is sometimes painful. But it happens every day. I cannot recall the last time something like that happened in politics or religion.
Carl Sagan, 1987 CSICOP Keynote Address

We are here on earth to do good for others. What the others are here for, I don't know.
W. H. Auden

Men of intemperate mind never can be free; their passions forge their fetters.
Edmund Burke

An enlightened human being should be humane, fair, kindly, wise, humorous, learned, brave, generous, honest, tolerant, and dedicated to doubt.
J.F.

In the Third World, in medicine, teaching, and in low-paid welfare positions, in areas that were covered in the past by missionaries, the work is still being done by people who often claim to be devout. Their work may be selfless and of benefit to humanity. But the 'devout'; 'the pious'; 'the strict'; 'the fundamentalist'; 'the orthodox'; 'the deeply religious' in general seem to me unbending rather than caring, judgemental rather than forgiving. They have pat answers to complex moral questions, because their priests have winnowed these answers from ancient texts disregarding the centuries of scientific and psychological research and learning which have superseded them. Ancient scriptures give to the pious answers without them having to think. Beautiful

at times these texts may be but it is hardly surprising that after two thousand years words written by and for primitive tribesmen are obscure and contradictory. They are ignorant of all we think of as knowledge, steeped in superstition, vengeance and mindless savagery. The pious are riddled with fear. Fear of transgression, fear of delight, fear of offending their unrelenting deity, fear of flouting traditions enforced by their forefathers, fear of heresy, fear of sexual longings, fear of scorn, fear of freedom from restraint, fear of the abyss, fear of guilt-free happiness. **And fear kills kindness and poisons joy.**
J.F.

I even occasionally convinced my father, and altered his opinion on some points of detail: which I state to his honour, not my own.
John Stuart Mill.

It is not enough that one simply has an unexamined belief that happens to be true; one must understand why the belief in question is the true one.
War is an ugly thing, but not the ugliest of things. The degraded state of moral and patriotic feeling which thinks that nothing is worth war is much worse. The person who has nothing for which he is willing to fight nothing which is more important than his own personal safety, is a miserable creature and has no chance of being free unless made and kept so by the exertions of better men than himself.
John Stuart Mill.

In Apartheid South Africa, blacks were taught to call whites 'Baas'. In Trinidad, 'Massa'.
When Trinidadians gained their freedom from their white masters, they called their Independence.
'Massa Day Done'.

People hate the Jews because they killed Jesus. Big deal! It was only for three days!

He has all the virtues I deplore and none of the vices I admire.
Winston Churchill

George Bernard Shaw inviting Churchill to the first night of *Major Barbara*: "Bring a friend, if you have one."
Churchill replied: "Can't make the first night. Will come to the second, if there is one."

All killers must be punished, unless they kill in very large numbers, and to the sound of trumpets.

As a playgoer at the Chichester Theatre arrived in my row to take her seat, I noticed that there was an empty seat on her right. We got into a conversation, and as tickets for this show were like gold dust, I asked her if she knew who would be sitting in the seat next to her. She explained that it had been booked for her husband. Looking at my watch I said "I'm afraid he's going to be late."
She said, "He's dead." I waited a discreet couple of minutes before pursuing our chat. "Why didn't you bring a family member, or a friend?" I asked her. "They're all at the funeral," she said.

Even if I were to meet such a learned and noble man as he was, my old heart could no longer receive the impression which twenty years ago it took as effortlessly as wax, one which will not dissolve until my heart does. Joseph Banks, on the death of his fellow voyager, "The amiable, easy-going and ever faithful Daniel Solander."

Stretching his hand up to reach the stars, too often man
forgets the flowers at his feet.
Jeremy Bentham

By striving to do the impossible, man has always achieved
what is possible. Those who have continuously done no
more than they believed possible, have never taken a
single step forward.
Mikhail Bakunin

The greatest remedy for anger is delay.
Time flies like an arrow. Fruit flies like a banana.
A chicken crossing the road is poultry in motion.

The perception that God cannot be benevolent is very old.
Plays by Aeschylus and Euripides make a quite explicit
statement that the gods are selfish and cruel, though they
expect better behaviour from humans.
Steven Weinberg

I would never die for my beliefs because I might be wrong.
Bertrand Russell

Men fear thought as they fear nothing else on earth –
more than ruin
more even than death… Thought is subversive and
revolutionary, destructive and terrible, thought is merciless to
privilege, established institutions, and comfortable habit.

Thought looks into the pit of hell and is not afraid. Thought is
great, swift and free, the light of the world, and the chief glory
of man.So far as I can remember, there is not one word in the
Gospels in praise of intelligence.
Bertrand Russell

There is something feeble and a little contemptible about a man whocannot face the perils of life without the help of comfortable myths. Almost inevitably, some part of him is aware that they are myths, and that he believes them only because they are comforting. Moreover, since he is aware, however dimly, that his opinions are not rational, he becomes furious when they are disputed.
Bertrand Russell

We do not speak of faith that two and two are four, or that the earth is round. We speak of faith when we wish to substitute emotion for evidence.

There are three kinds of people in the world: those who can count, and those who can't.

Science deals with physical reality by proposing hypotheses and testing them by observations designed to prove them wrong. Those hypotheses that survive become part of the provisional body of knowledge we call natural law.Applying that knowledge, by and large, has taken us from a state of miserable, disease-ridden ignorance to a stage where, for all its faults, many people in many countries have a decent material existence and a remarkable degree of control over their physical world.
Science survives because it works.
Dr John Haine, Cambridge

At the heart of religion is the proposition that some supernatural being, outside the universe as we know it, created physical reality. When a theologist can propose an experimental test which is capable of falsifying the hypothesis, then his subject might start to contribute something useful to our understanding. There is no evidence that any such creator exists. To my mind, whatever the sophistication of theology as an academic subject, theology has the same relation to science as astrology has to astronomy. As for the existence of academic departments devoted to theology, we must remember, first, that universities originally started as religious institutions; second, the close relationship in many societies between political power, education, and religion as a means of social control (which persists in some places to this day); third, the reluctance of any institution to vote (or study) itself out of existence.

I doubt that we have many professors of theology believing that the sooner all Christians ascend to heaven in a rapture while the rest of us burn, the better.

Richard Dawkins

It is hard to believe that health is improved by the semi-permanent state of morbid guilt suffered by a Roman Catholic possessed of normal human frailty and less than normal intelligence. Religion is basically guilt with different holidays.

Conscience is the inner voice that warns us that someone may be looking.

H. L. Menken

The deep, deep peace of the double bed after the hurly-burly of the chaise longue.

Mrs Patrick Campbell.

Roses are not things that my life is a bed of.
Branston, their dog, has what looks like an old-fashioned alarm clock strapped to his collar. It is a homing device – it zaps him if he strays beyond the garden. The frequency is the same as the dishwasher. When the
cycle reaches its climax, poor old Branston foams at the mouth and runs around the ceiling.

Roger Lewis:

(About Sybil Thorndike) Nobody loves anybody as much as Sybil loves everybody.
Noel Coward.

On a clear day you can see Marlowe. On a *very* clear day, you can see Marlow, Beaumont and Fletcher. Noel Coward to Edith Evans (during rehearsals for *Hay Fever*)
If you have nothing good to say about anybody, come and sit right by me. – Alice Roosevelt.
I love Brittany. I find the wild and primitive here. When my clogs resonate on this granite ground I hear the muffled powerful thud that I'm looking for in painting.
Paul Gaugin.

Of Sarah Bernhardt: 'Star Quality'.
She has the unique talent for endowing immobility with excitement.

Gemma Arterton was like a puppyish sun, trying to break through the smog hanging over the biggest coal-fired power station in China.
Christopher Hart on *The Master Builder*

'Shameless' and 'Shameful' , though seemingly opposite, mean almost the same... Like 'Priceless' and 'Invaluable'.
Ogni Mattina, in Africa, una gazzella si sveglia,
Sa ch dovra correre piu in fretta del leone, o verra uccisa
Ogni mattina, in Africa, un leone si sveglia
Sa che dovra correre piu della gazzella, o morrira di fame,
Quando il sole sorge, non importa se tu sei un leone o una gazzella, Cominci a correre.
Every morning in Africa a buck wakes up
He knows he must run faster than the lion or be his dinner
Every morning in Africa a lion wakes up
He knows he must run faster than the buck or
he'll die thinner,

If you're a lion or a buck,
When day beaks in Africaaaah
Run like fuck.
Queen Mummy Ju-Ju JF.

***

A gaze like a falcon looking through a Venetian blind
Martin Amis (of

Salman Rushdie)
Success is the ability to go from one failure to another with no loss of
enthusiasm.
Winston Churchill

I have dwelt all my life in the outer suburbs of human contempt and by
standing still I now inhabit the metropolis.
Quentin Crisp.

Time is a river. That which has been, is not; that which was not
Begins to be.
Ovid

My Barber, Napoleon. An Assyrian from Iraq. Assyrians are Christians.
Their language is akin to Aramaic. Napoleon has lived in Denmark for
twenty-seven years. Three children there with his first wife. In London, he
has two more.

Wives. Not children.

Religion is based on dogma and belief, science is based
on doubt and questioning. In religion, faith is a virtue. In
science, it is a vice.
JerryCoyne.

Burt Bacharach was Marlene Dietrich's arranger and
accompanist for five
years. They were neither married nor lovers. This is from her
autobiography: "Working with him was seventh heaven. As a
man, he
embodied everything a woman could wish for. How many
such men are
there? For me he was the only one."

Not everything that can be counted counts, and not
everything that counts
can be counted.
Albert Einstein

***

I don't want to wrong anybody, so I won't go so far as to
say that she actually wrote poetry, but her conversation, to
my mind, was of a nature calculated to excite the liveliest of
suspicions. Well, I mean to say, when a girl suddenly asks you
out of a blue sky if you don't sometimes feel that the stars are
God's daisy-chain, you begin to think a bit.
I suppose half the time Shakespeare just shoved down
anything that came into his head.

A ray of sunshine and a Scotsman with a grievance are
not easily confused.
A melancholy-looking man, he had the appearance of
someone who had
searched for the leak in life's gas pipe with a lighted candle.
I always advise people never to give advice.

A scone of yesterday's making. – P.G. Woodhouse.

***

"You're Marlowe?"
I nodded.
"I'm a little disappointed," he said. "I rather expected
something with dirty fingernails."
"Come inside," I said, "and you can be witty sitting down."
Raymond Chandler, *The High Window*

***

As he sat there semi-helpless, with his stump exposed,
there was more each morning for a boy who worshipped
him to worship, and what there was to pity was a little less
impossible to bear.
Philip Roth, *The Plot Against America*

I cheered at the banderillero's display,
As they stuck the bull in their own clever way,
For I hadn't had so much fun since the day
My brother's dog Rover
Got run over.
Tom Lehrer

My wife's arse is so big, she's taller sitting down than she
is standing up.
Les Dawson

Sudden Prayers Make God Jump. Original title for my autobiography.

James Hogan, my publisher, said if I kept it, the book would be put on the shelf under 'Religion'. He suggested CLOSE UP....I can't complain. It was a Best Seller.

The Suffragen Bishop of Thrings,
Had no time for tarts and such things,
His height of desire
Was a boy in the choir
With a bum like a jelly on springs.

There are US Presidential hopefuls who refuse to accept evolution. There are those who think that the collection of chemicals that is an eight-cell embryo has an immortal soul.
Sam Harris

***

Every person in this audience knows more – much more – than the men who wrote the scriptures. They knew nothing of physics, chemistry, medical science, astronomy, cosmology, differential calculus, chaos theory, particle physics, psychology, philosophy, sociology, neuroscience, cognitive behavioural therapy, ancient history, anthropology, archaeology, demographics, nothing of Plato, Aristotle, Isaac Newton, Voltaire, or the Enlightenment; nothing of Charles Darwin and Evolution. They had never read Confucius, the Mahabharata, Tolstoy, Dante, Goethe or the plays of William Shakespeare.

We can have ethical and spiritual lives without lying to ourselves and to others and without pretending to be certain about things we are clearly not certain about.
In attempting to find a middle ground between religious dogmatism and intellectual honesty, it seems to me that religious moderates betray faith and reason equally.
By refusing to question the legitimacy of raising children to believe that they are Christians, Muslims and Jews— religious moderates tacitly support the religious divisions in our world.

They also perpetuate the myth that a person must believe things on insufficient evidence in order to have an ethical and spiritual life. While religious moderates don't fly planes into buildings, or organise their lives around apocalyptic prophecy, they refuse to deeply question the preposterous ideas of those who do.

I have no doubt that there are millions of nice Mormons who are tolerant of dissent and perfectly cordial toward homosexuals. Does this, in your view, even slightly increase the probability that the Book of Mormon was delivered on golden plates to Joseph Smith Jr. by the angel Moroni? Do all the good Muslims in the world lend credence to the claim that Muhammad flew to heaven on a winged horse? Do all the good pagans throughout history suggest that Mt. Olympus was ever teeming with invisible gods? The alleged usefulness of religion—the fact that it sometimes gets people to do very good things indeed—is not an argument for its truth. Religion gets people to do good things for bad reasons when good reasons are actually available.
It also gets people to do very bad things that they would not otherwise do.

There are at this very moment perfectly ordinary Shia and Sunni Muslims drilling holes into each other's brains with power tools in the suburbs of Baghdad. What are the chances they would be doing this without the "benefit" of their incompatible religious identities?

Whoso eateth my flesh, and drinketh my blood, hath eternal life; and I will raise him up at the last day. For my flesh is meat indeed, and my blood is drink indeed.!!!!!!!!!
Martin Luther quoting the Bible

The high unclouded summer of the world…
"The ancient and unchanging faith of the Church" does

change a little from time to time. Being bogus to a remarkable degree, it has to. The fact that the current Pope freely uses terms like 'reason' and 'truth' does not at all guarantee that he is on good terms with the former, or would recognise the latter if it bit him.

Sam Harris

Isaac Newton spent the period between the summer of 1665 and the spring of 1667 working in isolation and dodging an outbreak of plague that was laying waste to the pious men and women of England. When he emerged from his solitude, he had invented the differential and integral calculus, established the field of optics, and discovered the laws of motion and universal gravitation. Many scientists consider this to be the most awe-inspiring display of human intelligence in man's history.

Religion gets people to do good things for bad reasons, when good reasons are actually available.

In sport, battle with heart, lose with dignity, and win with grace.

Birds soar, not by defying the elements but by exploiting them. I'd rather sing one wild song and burst my heart with it than live a thousand years watching my digestion and being afraid of the wet.

Jack London

***

While performing in Tunis, we were invited to stay with the American Ambassador Johannes van der Vries the Third and his wife in their beautiful Arabian palace in Carthage. She called him 'Hanny' and he called her 'Ellie', in my experience the only naming option there seems to be for distinguished American matrons.

A tiny rivulet ran right through the middle of the palace, gurgling over smooth pebbles of marble, and cascading into little pools of crystal-clear water perfumed with sandalwood and patchouli. Ellie was a horney old broad of around seventy. Her extravagant manner suggested she was starring in her own private movie of *Gone With The Wind* – not like Vivien Leigh which might have been kind of acceptable, but surprisingly - like the Big Black Servant played by the wonderful Hattie McDaniel.

***

Every single member of our species homo sapiens has spread round the world today from the same human ancestors conceived in a cave in the Rift Valley in Africa at the dawn of time. These black-skinned people's gradually developing brains worked out that seeds become plants if you water them, that they grow tall and double their yield if you fertilise them. This and the domestication of cows, chickens, goats and oxen in a climate free of tsetse flies, allowed fortunate humans in the Fertile Crescent to prosper uniquely within the time afforded them when they no longer had to spend their every moment foraging for berries, seeds, roots, tasty herbs and hunting prey to exist.

Black white and every conceivable variation in between that exists in the world today, every member of the species homo sapiens has a black ancestor born in the Rift Valley in Africa when our world was young. That's where we come from. All of us. So race is a social construct, it's evolution moulded over thousands of years, by geography, climate, the domestication of fowl, cattle and draught animals, and the availability of resources.

Like a stick of Brighton Rock, Ellie was white all the way through, but perhaps her impersonation of Hattie McDaniel was close to a primal truth. She felt closer to the *essence* of the Big Black Maid than she did to the wan milksops of the women of her traditional class. She had shaved off her eyebrows, and way above the light stubble which remained at the end of this cosmetic manoeuvre – or perhaps she had a kind of alopecia of the eyebrows – but in any case, with a thick black pencil she had drawn two perfect semi-circles a finger's width above the ridge where normal brows are expected to sprout. This facial geometry may have been the height of chic in Paris in the twenties, but now she looked so startled it was hard not to laugh. She took my chin in her meaty paw and squeezed hard to a make my lips pucker up. " Who's a pretty boy?" she gargled, re-arranging her wrinkled features in preparation for delivering an almighty smacker. "Are you married?" she gargled again. I kept deathly still – imagining a hungry octopus landing on my face. " Are you shackin' up?" Our noses were touching. Humiliatingly, I began to tremble.

"Or do you Jess Fant – ah Saa-ahzzz - like the rest of us?" 'Fantasise' is what I eventually worked out was what she was aiming to convey. I straightened up, re-asserting my dignity. I didn't tell her the truth – times were different then – and as she was our hostess, I didn't fuck with her fantasies.

J.F.

For every complicated problem there is a solution that is simple, direct, understandable, and wrong.

H. L. Mencken

Ignorance is the position from which we work out
what is best.
Richard Dawkins.

On the Crucifixion
Why the architect of the universe, the divine mathematician, devisor of the laws of physics, of quantum mechanics, of the carefully tuned physical constants, this paragon of superhuman intellect, was unable to think of a better way to forgive the sins of one species of African ape than to have himself tortured and killed as a blood sacrifice…

***

A: What do you call a deer with only one eye?
B: No idea.
A: What do you call a deer with only one eye and paralysed, so he can't move?
B: Still no idea.
A: What do you call a deer with only one eye and paralysed, with no genitals?
B: Still no fuckin' idea.

Courage is the quality which guarantees all others.
Winston Churchill

Courage is useless without good judgment.
For a fulfilled life, the indispensable virtue is kindness.
J.F.

In attempting to find a middle ground between religious dogmatism and intellectual honesty, religious moderates betray faith and reason equally.

***

In Lahore for her father The Governor General's meeting with the Maharajah, the Hon. Emily Eden, the more caustic of Lord Auckland's daughters reported that Ranjit Singh had a grand total of thirty-two wives. His eldest son, with whom Emily had had a mild flirtation, had not responded to her overtures. "He rarely responds to anyone," Emily complained in a letter to Lady Auckland. "He barely opens his lips." Lady Auckland warned her daughter by return "Karak Singh is a blockhead and a slave to opium. He has passed his whole life in a state of stupefaction."

In spite of Ranjit Singh's thirty-two wives – or perhaps because of them – the Maharajah had adopted an eighteen-year-old Sikh young man of great beauty called Hira Singh, from whom he was totally inseparable. Claiming indeed that "Hira Singh alone can lull me to sleep" was Ranjit Singh's explanation for the otherwise curious fact that the beautiful Sikh, his young jaw faintly outlined by his incipient beard, his moustache hardly more than a shadow outlining his rosebud lips, spent every night, all night, clasped in the much-married Maharajah's loving arms.

In any other country, the manner by which Hira Singh achieved his rapid advancement at the Maharajah's Court would have rendered him infamous, but in Lahore, the beautiful young man was looked up to and respected.

The Gubernatorial Entourage was setting off for the Maharajah's Palace a short distance across the *maidan*, when Paranjit, the Honourable Emily's faithful groom sprinted from the stables leading his mistress's gelding, jingling and sparkling with freshly burnished tack. More sedate transport to the Palace, on a *howdah* had been politely declined by the young lady. Mounting Freddie, and joyfully kicking up a dust, the Honourable Emily shouted over her shoulder to anyone who would listen :-

"I can't stand much more elephant."

Inspired by John Keay's *The Tartan Turban*

***

The madness of 'Romantic Love'.
Taunt me, and hurt me
Deceive me, desert me
I'm yours till I die
So in love with you am I…

And the charm of it:
So nice to waken with
So nice to sit down to eggs and bacon with..
Oh how we'd thrive
In a cottage for two
Or even three, four or five
If you could see
Your future with me
Then you would be
So ee-
Zy to love…

***

The invisible and the nonexistent look very much alike.
Gran at ninety: on hearing that another old friend had gone:
"It's like the bleedin' Burma Railway."
A Conservative is a Liberal with a teenage daughter.

***

We go to liberate, not to conquer.
Be ferocious in battle, but remember to be
magnanimous in victory.
Iraq is the site of the Garden of Eden, of the Great Flood and
the birthplace of Abraham.
Tread lightly there.
If there are casualties of war then remember that when they
woke up and got dressed in the morning they did not plan to
die this day.

Allow them dignity in death.
Bury them properly and mark their graves.
There will be no time for sorrow.
Let's bring everyone home and leave Iraq a better place for
us havingbeen there.
Our business now is north.
Colonel Tim Collins.

Like the beat beat beat of the tom-tom
When the jungle shadows fall
Like the tick tick tock of the stately clock
As it stands against the wall
Like the drip drip drip of the raindrops
When the summer shower is through
So a voice within me keeps repeating you, you, you
Night and day, you are the one
Only you beneath the moon and under the sun
Whether near to me, or far
It's no matter darling where you are
I think of you
Night and day, day and night, why is it so
That this longing for you follows wherever I go
In the roaring traffic's boom
In the silence of my lonely room
I think of you
Night and day, Night and day
Under the hide of me
There's an oh such a hungry yearning burning inside of me
And its torment won't be through
'Til you let me spend my life making love to you
Day and night, night and day.
Begin the Beguine, Night and Day, Let's fall in love..
Easy to Love
Shakespeare and Mozart are right up there
with Cole Porter.
J.F.

Othello, V.ii. 341-354 (Heartbroken, immediately after smothering his beloved wife Desdemona on suspicion of infidelity, a false charge planted by the dastardly Iago.)
To his attendants:
Speak of me as I am. Then must you speak
Of one that loved not wisely but too well,
Of one not easily jealous but, being wrought,
Perplexed in the extreme; of one whose hand,
Like the base Indian, threw a pearl away
Richer than all his tribe; of one whose subdued eyes,
Albeit unused to the melting mood,
Drop tears as fast as the Arabian trees
Their medicinable gum. Set you down this,
And say besides that in Aleppo once,
Where a malignant and a turbaned Turk
Beat a Venetian and traduced the state,
I took by the throat the circumcised dog
And smote him thus…
(He kills himself with his sword.)

***

To the families of the fallen in the Civil War:
I feel how weak and fruitless must be any word of mine which should attempt to beguile you from the grief of a loss so overwhelming. But I cannot refrain from tendering you the consolation that may be found in the thanks of the Republic they died to save.

I pray that our Heavenly Father may assuage the anguish of your bereavement, and leave you only the cherished memory of the loved and lost and the solemn pride that must be yours to have laid so costly a sacrifice upon the altar of freedom.
Yours very sincerely and respectfully, **A. Lincoln.**
To a grieving widow, whose husband was killed in Niger:
"He knew what he signed up for."
Donald Trump

Predating Religions of the Book, Judaism,
Christianity and Islam,
by A THOUSAND YEARS.
Fragment carved into A Funerary Monument from
3rd. Century B.C.
Al Khanum. Hellenistic City in Afghanistan:
On The River Oxus
As a child, learn good manners.
As a young man, learn to control your passions.
In middle age, be just.
Strive always to be kind.
In old age, give good advice
And die without regret
No mention of a Prophet, a Saviour, let alone a Jealous God.
No paradise for good behaviour nor any threat of everlasting
Torment in
Hell – for getting it wrong.

DIEGO

The old man looked as if he was screaming. A stroke had blasted his peasant features and the hand which clawed at the rail of the outside staircase was clenched in a permanent fist. Lowering himself a step at a time, Rodolfo reached the cobbled yard of his farmhouse where his three-wheeler stood at an angle to the dry-stone wall.

At full speed the two-stroke engine of these diminutive vehicles buzzes like a swarm of bees so it is called an *Ape* (pronounced Ah-pay) which means bee. A motor scooter on the other hand, world famous for a while when Gregory Peck took Audrey pillion round the sights in *Roman Holiday*, is called a *Vespa* which means wasp.

The *Ape* rattled into life. Rodolfo swivelled its little wheels towards the deeply rutted track which led down onto the metalled road. When you see an *Ape* sharing the road with normal motor-cars, the way they jaunt along at a leisurely pace eschewing the universal race to beat all comers and cut a minute off your journey, they make you feel good about the world.

Until people tell you about Diego…

You never see farmers or fishermen wearing glasses; wide horizons keep your vision toned. Sergio and Richetta's youngest grandchild, Diego, always wore glasses. He was the last of the farming line.

In rural Tuscany, life has hardly changed since the Bronze Age. Ploughing, sowing and planting in the spring, reaping and harvesting in the summer, gathering the fruit, tending the flocks, treading the grapes, making the cheese, collecting wood from the forests for winter fuel.

Sergio and Richetta are the fountainhead of a prodigious family. Five children of their own, and a score of grandchildren, ending with Diego. They are old now, sinewy with years of unremitting labour. Neither of them can read or write.

When I first arrived I asked Richetta for the telephone number of the plumber. She disappeared and returned with a piece of paper and a stub of pencil which she handed to me.

Only when I was ready to write, did she carefully pronounce the dialling code plus the six digits that I required. All the numbers she needs are in her head.

Along with the farmhouse which has been in his family for generations, Sergio inherited a large flock of sheep and an estate consisting of eighty hectares of oak forest – ideal fuel for wood-burning stoves – thirty of arable land for cultivating maize and tobacco, a hillside of vineyards, three orchards – apple and pear – cherry and peach. The milk from the sheep is made into *peccorino* cheese. They breed pigs in the barn, geese and chickens and ducks in the yard, and rabbits in the dark, cabined in a row of knocked up hutches.

Their vegetable garden is a never-ending cornucopia. With nothing to spend their money on but their daughters' weddings, after years of unimaginably hard work and agricultural subsidies, the old couple are rich.

Scholarly, clownish with a smattering of English, Diego played 'Volare' on his keyboard and video-games on his computer. His mischievous smile belied his tendency to blush. Blushing is usually a sign of timidity, but Diego was as timid as a lion.

His mother was a primary school-teacher, but that didn't stop her being a glamour puss. Her ample figure was often squeezed into 'outfits' of fearless originality which she had made herself, her hair has been every colour of the spectrum sometimes all at once, and the earrings which she favours could accommodate a brace of budgerigars.

Diego inherited Milena's dark, laughing eyes. And Candido's obstinate chin. Candido is a master carpenter and a passionate hunter. He keeps his pack of pedigree boar-hounds on his father's farm, and they ululate with frustration in their kennels throughout the long hot summer till the hunting season begins.

The young couple's pride in their only child was the keystone of their existence. They denied him nothing: his mountain bike had twin lurex panniers and fifteen gears, his keyboard had a microphone and speakers for impromptu concerts. He had a state-of-the-art Apple-Mac, diving gear for summer and skis for winter. This lavish indulgence should have made the boy insufferable, but his parents' extravagance had been tempered with agrarian good sense and he had been taught good manners.

Diego was a little prince.

Monte Santa Maria Tiberina is a tiny mediaeval city perched like an eagle's eyrie on an Umbrian Apennine in the province of Perugia. Candido and Milena's home is built up against the rock just below the castle at the summit of the escarpment, which can be reached only after a dizzying climb through narrow streets and stairways inaccessible to motor transport. The natives of this mountain stronghold have calves like sherpas. They resort to donkey carts for heavy loads. Some are not deterred from

coaxing their two-stroke-engines as far as the church of Santa Maria Tiberina halfway up. Bees and wasps both buzz ferociously as they attack the vertiginous gradients, skidding on the ancient cobbles, polished by centuries of shoe-leather to the patina of glass.

It was the Festa of San Giorgio and pupils of the Scuola Media Statale had been given the day off. Diego woke at his usual hour, and was halfway into his uniform before he remembered that it was a holiday. Squirming into his jeans and cleaning his glasses on his t-shirt before pulling it over

his head, he burst into the kitchen, helped himself to lukewarm coffee from the stove, while grabbing a pastry from the fridge on his way to the door. He called to his mother who was at her sewing-machine in the work-room,

"Ciao, Mama!"

Mounting his bike, he freewheeled down the Vicolo dei Soldati his hands behind his head, steering the bicycle with his knees like a jockey riding bareback, past balconies festooned with trailing geraniums, till he came to the little piazza where the solitary shop and bar nestled forlornly in the shade of an abandoned mill. The old men of the town sat on plastic chairs smoking and slapping their cards down on the Formica-topped table in a noisy game of *scopa*. This rustic *vignette* didn't tempt the village lad to linger.

At the bottom of the mountain is a *diga*, a small reservoir built by Rodolfo to conserve the winter rains for his tobacco fields in the dry season. This modest stretch of water is a magnet for local youngsters, the epicentre for aquatic sports of infinite variety. In the height of summer, of course, bathing in your underwear is popular. Since almost no country-bred Italian child can swim, their attempts to propel themselves through the water cause much noise and effort and hilarity. Skidding flat stones across the surface, and hurling larger stones at a bottle or a can to try and sink it can be played in all weathers. As can catching frogs or yellow-bellied salamanders (with only a moderate rate of success), fishing with a cane and a bent pin (one hundred percent futile – only good for shouting and splashing and dunking as many of your friends as possible.)

Warnings from parents and elders of the very real danger of drowning are flouted, but since these exploits, for maximum enjoyment, require an audience, there is no inducement for solitary bathing, and to date, mercifully, there have been no tragedies. Rodolfo was Diego's great uncle (his grandfather Sergio's much younger brother), and he had spent his adult life jealously cultivating his rancour. The ancient laws of primogeniture in Italy have been superseded by the Napoleonic Code, which on the death of a parent bestows equal legacies on all the offspring. Sergio and Rodolfo's father had died young, however, when Rodolfo was still a child, and due to negligence on the lawyer's part, or cunning on Sergio's, the lion's share of their father's estate had gone uncontested to the eldest brother, Sergio.

Over the years Rodolfo had watched his older brother flourish with ever more bitterness in his heart. A melancholy-looking man even before he suffered his stroke, he had the appearance of someone who had searched for the leak in life's gas pipe with a lighted candle (rf. P.G. Woodhouse). This resentment of his sibling extended to Sergio's children and his children's children, to wives and husbands, to in-laws, to cousins and to sundry faithful pets. On the occasions when his path crossed that of any member of Sergio's numerous family, which was at only one remove from his own, Rodolfo's thrombotic rictus would harden like a cleft in a cliff of granite.

Since Rodolfo had constructed the *diga* specifically to supply the needs of his thirsty tobacco plants, he guarded the reservoir as jealously as he guarded his reputation and his umbrage.

Sebastiano, just turned seventeen, was flaunting his disdain for the juveniles frolicking in the water, while leaning on his bicycle and nonchalantly smoking a *Nazionale.* He was the first to hear the familiar buzz of the *Ape* approaching down the hill.

"Attenzione!" he yelled.

Diego was the last out of the water, shivering in his underpants, rummaging for his glasses in the pocket of his jeans.

The little cripple had grabbed a broken branch lying on the ground on his way up the bank of the *diga* and was swiping the air with it in ferocious anticipation of laying into this gaggle of ragamuffins. The gang, grabbing at their clothes and donning their trainers at a hop, leapt onto their bicycles and wobbled out of harm's way. They reassembled at the foot of the bank, however, to watch Diego catch it.

Which he did. But the scene had lost its savour through repetition. As the summer

wore on, the regular confrontation became more savage which added spice to their aquatic escapades.

As each member of the gang egged the others on, the youngsters lost all moral compass. Since the joyless old bastard had had his stroke, there was the delicious satisfaction of baiting the afflicted – of mocking his limping gait and brandishing twisted fists at his lop-sided snarl.

Rodolfo had left his *Ape* with the motor running. The gang stood leaning on their bicycles , agog, in anticipation of Diego's humiliation at the hands of his uncle.

Abandoning his clothes and his bicycle, in a split second of rashness, fuelled by his burgeoning testosterone and the rapt attention of his gang, Diego leapt into the driving seat of the three-wheeler. He had driven Candido's tractor clamped between his father's knees since he was four years old. This was the extent of his driving experience. The two-stroke engine roared as he pushed the accelerator to the floor. When he reached the road at the top, the little *Ape* pounced onto the tarmac like a panther on a snake.

It wasn't going fast but it was suddenly in front of him –a wall of steel not just in front, but filling the whole windscreen. A ten-ton pantechnicon that spanned the whole width of the mountain road. There was almost never any traffic on the road to Monte Santa Maria Tiberina. The winding strip of tarmac was too narrow for passing – sheer drops on both sides…

The *Ape* flew off the mountain like an eagle before it stoops. As Sebastiano was heading for the town, he caught a momentary glimpse of a silhouette against the sun, a raggedy sort of glider, he thought… The *Maresciallo* did his best to dissuade Milena and Candido from visiting the mortuary in Perugia, but they were resolute.

When the sheet was withdrawn from Diego's broken corpse, his head was between his shoulders, exactly where you would expect it to be. Candido had been warned in a whisper by the *Maresciallo* the horrifying truth of what had happened when the little three-wheeler hurtled out of the sky onto the rocks below. Diego's head lad been ripped from his sixteen- year- old hairless torso. An unearthly sound escaped Milena's throat. It was the sound Candido's boar-hounds made when the hunting season began. Candido held his wife so tightly there was no breath left in her body. Diego's glasses had been carefully set on the bridge of his marble-white nose.

Was this an act of kindness, to make Diego's severed head look like the studious boy who had just died? Or was it a cruel joke like sticking a moustache onto a snowman? At the funeral, Don Ottorino in his everyday chasuble and stole broke down and could not be comforted. Everybody knew everybody else in this tiny mountain community, so Don Ottorino's congregation, were not just his parishioners, but in in a real sense his flock – his family.

It was hard to decipher the benediction engulfed as it was in the Priest's muffled sobs, but Milena claimed later that Don

Ottorino had assured her that Diego would sit on the Right Hand of God. "He will remain young and beautiful forever," he assured her, "in the memories of all who loved him and in the eyes of Our Blessed Lord."

Milena clung onto her husband like a tigress to her prey. When her knees gave way the couple subsided onto the turf as one, like felons shackled together in chains. A tragedy of this magnitude changes the relations of all those embroiled in it. Sometimes it can drive the bereaved apart, the pain experienced is so devastating people need to find something or someone to blame besides God. And even love can turn to rancour.

Candido was handsome, with a reputation as a Lothario. He was often home late for dinner. From the day of Diego's death, however, when he wasn't in his workshop, Candido dropped out of the *Briscola* tournament at the *Bar Extra*, and after the hunt he cut short the celebrations there with his fellow hunters.

After work he would pop in to see his mother, and help Sergio with odd jobs round the farm or tending the vegetable garden before getting home early to eat his pasta at the table in silence with Milena. Everything had already been said. Often he would hold her hand the way they used to do when they were courting, still by habit surreptitiously, as if expecting to be rebuked.   By next summer Milena was pregnant again, and her smile returned tremulously when she told her husband that her periods had stopped. Candido longed for a girl. No boy could hope to compete with his Little Prince. When the contractions started, Candido telephoned Bianca who had helped deliver Diego. She was there in ten minutes on her Lambretta Candido gripped Milena's naked foot as the pains came closer and closer together. Milena gasped and pushed with all her might, and suddenly the tiny featherless nestling popped out – scarlet from his mother's womb. Bianca held the creature by the feet. Assuming a business-like manner, she smacked the child hard between the shoulder blades. From the piercing cry of indignation, the young couple didn't have to look between the baby's legs to know it was a boy.   Another boy. It was the beginning of his life, but it was also the beginning of a new life for Milena and Candido. Two miracles took place that day. First, the arrival of their wrinkled red and noisy offspring into the world; followed directly by an overwhelming joy and wonder at the power of their love for the new scrap of humanity that lay on Milena's breast, his perfect little mouth already sucking on the air in anticipation. Candido lay on the bed beside his wife, their baby between them. A family again.

And not little by little, but suddenly like a thunderbolt, their broken hearts began to mend.

They called the boy Mirco. Milena's choice. It was in fashion. They gave Diego's keyboard and speakers to Bianca's son Edouardo who had expressed his dreams of forming a band. Mirco was a gentle child.

Outside fairy tales, princes don't come along often.

He was no good at football. Nor at anything else much. But he loved everybody.

And everybody loved him back.

***

Invitation to an Assassin

ISLAM
What no Muslim dare think.

The notion that any ancient book could be an infallible guide to living in the present gets my vote for being the most misguided and dangerous idea on earth.
Sam Harris

Anyone who thinks he knows for sure that Jesus was born of a virgin or that the Qur'an is the perfect word of the Creator of the universe is lying. Either he is lying to himself or to everyone else. In neither case should such false certainties be celebrated.
Sam Harris.

A man can have sex with animals such as sheep, cows, camels and so on. However, he should kill the animal after he has his orgasm. He should not sell the meat to the people in his own village, but selling the meat to the next- door village should be fine.
Ayatollah Khomeni/ *Tahrirolvasyleh***.**

If a wife dies, it is permitted for the husband to have sex with her corpse up to ten hours after her death. – Recent pronouncement by an Imam.

Islam's critics are silenced by a very real threat of murder. Maajid Nawaaz of the Quilliam Foundation is a courageous defender of Islam in the face of all the recent horrors of IslamISM. As a crusader against extremism he insists that Islam is a religion of peace.

In The National Museum in Lahore I have gaped in awe at a mighty scimitar covered in microscopic script. The whole of the Qu'ran is engraved upon it, on both sides of the cruelly curving blade. It is claimed that the scribes who etched these sacred verses into this instrument of slaughter went blind in the process. The savagery in "The Book" is often excused by "These were the times," when the tribes were in a state of constant war. Jesus, Buddha, Confucius, Socrates all preceded Mohammed by hundreds of years, and their gentleness, wisdom and their tolerance are celebrated to this day. Even the other religions of "The Book" – Christianity and Judaism, in the 21st Century – do not treat their scriptures as the unalterable and infallible words of the God Head with Death as the penalty for anyone who disagrees. At the moment Muslims amount to less than 23% of the world's population. That leaves 77% of the rest of us to be slaughtered or converted. That should keep Jihadists busy. Furthermore, Islamists seek Death for Muslims deemed not pious enough: sacrilege, blasphemy, missing prayers, infringements of any of the thousands of laws and prohibitions applying to every aspect of a true believer's life in the seventh century. Islamists are addicted to beheadings and to the religious intoxication induced by the fountain of blood issuing from the necks of the infidels. (The Qu'ran's succinct command is "to strike at the neck" of all disbelievers.) The executioners' ecstatic cries of *"Allahu Akbar!"* confirm that they are doing God's Holy Work.

***

What is the common factor that connects all the slaughter throughout the
Middle East today?

Islam.

Muslims' belief in the divinity and hence the infallibility of the Book is the main cause of the horrors unleashed by Jihadists today. Their conviction that this life is merely a painful prelude to

Hell or to Paradise; a testing ground for the eternity to follow, where sinners will roast forever for their misdemeanours.

The Key to Paradise is to slaughter as many unbelievers as possible by strapping bombs to your bosom and blowing yourself up in the midst of infidels in the name of Allah, becoming a Martyr revered by fellow Muslims, who may also be jealous of the limitless Totty promised to martyrs in Paradise, a harem of beautiful virgins -seventy-five is an oft repeated number which may be apocryphal - but <u>plenty</u> at least to get young warriors keen for the task ahead.

Is it any wonder there is a scramble for suicide vests.

Following divinely inspired infallible texts cruelly misleads uneducated people – the populations of most countries in AD 600 and sadly even up to the present day – who believe what they are told by those in authority. In Islamic societies those in authority are Ayatollahs and Imams.

What happened to The Golden Age of Islam, six hundred years from the eighth to the fourteenth century in Baghdad and all across North Africa into Spain, its people conquered by Mohammed's invincible armies and given two choices – convert to Islam or have your head cut off.

But along with religion and military might, the invaders also brought culture. In Cordoba, scholars' works were collected there in the Great Library from all over the known world. Aristotle was translated into Arabic and saved forever for posterity.

Exquisite poetry, ravishing architecture, ornately decorated tiles, punctuated by quotations from the Qu'ran in flowing Arabic script to remind viewers that all this beauty was a gift from Allah. Astronomers mapped the heavens, mathematicians elucidated logarithms and invented algebra.

When I was a boy Arabia was the most exotic place in the world. Harems full of gorgeous *houris* lounged on hills of cushions, next to waterfalls spilling into turquoise pools. In the background, turbaned youths danced seductively to the tapping of skin drums and the swooping cries of a silver flute. Bearded sheiks galloped over the dunes, slashing the air with their scimitars, while veiled women clutched their hearts at the sight of them. White-bearded elders squatted sharing their memories over their hubble-bubbles, while a Nubian servant in a red fez poured coffee from a swan-necked pot.

Was I remembering a painting by Delacroix or Alma Tadema or any of the scores of orientalist painters who were inspired by sumptuous scenes of the newly discovered 'East'? I was not alone in thinking the Islamic world to be the cat's pyjamas.

In the City of Dreams, on Sunset Boulevard , the sexiest hotel in Hollywood was called 'The Garden of Allah'.

"Here with a loaf of bread beneath the bough, a flask of wine, a book of verse and thou, beside me in the wilderness, and wilderness is paradise enow…"

Reading Omar Khayyam made me feel like a sultan. A loaf of bread I could manage, Palgrave's Golden Treasury I could snaffle from my sister, a bottle of plonk, done. All I needed now was a bough and a "thou" to share it with. No one sprang to mind…. What happened to one of the greatest intellectual explosions in world history to rival that of Aristotle, Socrates, Homer and the great playwrights in Ancient Greece? Muhammad ibn Abdul Wahabi happened. He was an eighteenth century cleric who thought Islam had lost its way. It had splintered into so many sects there was nothing but constant war – killing and murderous strife.

The way forward, Wahabi maintained, was to revert to a literal reading of the Qu'ran. His revision made modernising, or tampering with The Holy book – *haram* – forbidden by Allah. This 'Reformation' resulted in the sanction of seventh century violence against Infidels, the hate-filled doctrine of Political IslamISM, the inspiration for all of today's *Jihadists.* The corollary to this religious reform was a ban on Joy. Later reformers of Christianity used the same tactic, notably Calvin in Europe and John Knox in Scotland, promoting guilt and the fear of Hell as the Church's principal dogma.

IslamISM will continue to tear the world apart until 'moderate' Muslims and above all Ayatollahs condemn political Islamism utterly and unambiguously. So far the deafening silence from Imams that meets every new Islamist atrocity can only be interpreted as approval – seventh century Muslims against the drunken, Godless West. Muslims dancing in the streets of New York after 9.11, another Milestone in the Bloody Battle to Islamicise the World.

Since the perfect word of God was transcribed in the seventh century AD, you'd think intellectuals like Maajid Nawaaz would concede that as a Muslim's only guide to living, The Qu'ran has not been an unqualified success. There are now more schisms, more divergency of interpretation within The Faith, more loathing and murder than ever before. Does any Muslim dare to question the value of a Text that has been the cause of more hatred and bloodshed than any other document in history?

After every atrocity, decent law-abiding "moderate" Muslims keep their heads down and their lips sealed. Why don't they march in their thousands to their favoured Mosques or to Parliament with banners proclaiming "NOT IN OUR NAME!" Witness the *millions* of demonstrators, almost the whole population of Hong Kong jamming the streets in protest at the extradition of "criminals" to the mainland, even knowing that dissent is never leniently dealt with under Xi Jinping. These millions of Marchers have so far succeeded in halting the extradition law…

Muslems' silence after jihadists' outrages masks their approval, or - like the dancers in the streets of New York after 9.11 - their jubilation. The Qu'ran cannot be held responsible, however, for extinguishing half of the human race, arguably the gentler half (females) in *purdah.* The veil is a relic of prehistory and its widespread use today is entirely due to the untrammelled zeal of Muslim patriarchs who will go to any lengths to retain their ascendancy and control over their females. By keeping their women wrapped up, they reason that they eliminate the remotest chance of their being duped into raising another man's child. But, sadly it is the women who vie among themselves to display the greatest piety and the most abject humility, to preen to their peers and ingratiate themselves to their menfolk.

Islam means Submission.

Many have black gauze sewn into the viewing apertures in their niqabs, so that even their eyes are invisible to an onlooker. They wear tight black gloves, to protect them from an inadvertent brush against an Infidel, and they would no more think of shaking hands with a man, than they would strip to their underwear and play football in Piccadilly Circus. The words of the great Ayaan Hirsi Ali…

Escaping an arranged marriage in Somalia she fled to Holland:

"This was an Infidel country, whose way of life we Muslims were supposed to oppose and reject. Why was it, then, so much better run, better led, and made for such better lives than the places we came from? Shouldn't the places where Allah was worshipped and his laws obeyed have been at peace and wealthy, and the unbelievers' countries ignorant, poor and at war? What was wrong with us? Why should Infidels have peace and Muslims be killing each other, when we were the ones who worshipped the True God?"

Democracy took hundreds of years to develop. Though the loathsome Spanish Inquisition began in 1231, and ran for seven hundred years, it was not finally banned until 1894. Crusades, religious persecution, the burning of witches and heretics, were atrocities perpetrated in Christianity's Dark Ages. The Reformation, the Enlightenment, the Age of Reason, Darwin, Freud, Galileo, Isaac Newton, Scientists and Historians in search of The Truth have eroded trust in ancient texts and helped to 'secularise' Christendom.

Christians today acknowledge that the savagery of the Old Testament is ancient folklore. Universal education, equal for both sexes, has opened our eyes to world history, psychology, the natural sciences as well as everything else that makes us a civilised society. The unaltered Qu'ran is the root and branch of Islamism. A selective reading of the Qu'ran encourages the poisonous efflorescence of Islamism to flourish. There are 34,000 Saudi-financed Madrassas in Pakistan at this moment, training the priests of the future to go out and conquer the infidel world just as The Prophet did in the seventh century with his ferocious armies.   Since Western philosophy and literature are *haram*, Wahabi fundamentalist teacher-priests promote only the Study of the Qu'ran, the Hadith (sayings of the Prophet), and Islamic Sharia Law. Many of the students learn by rote some verses and often the entire Holy Qu'ran to blazon their piety to their Muslim brethren even when a great many do not speak or understand Arabic. As they commit by rote to memory, the students rock to and fro like caged beasts at the end of their tether. If you start at the age of three along with your family, kneeling in submission five times a day every day for the rest of your life, reciting "There is no God but Allah, and Muhammad is his Messenger," what chance is there of ever being able to question the certainties of such ingrained beliefs?

Salafi and Wahabi Imams have interpreted their ancient scriptures to ban music of any kind, libraries, television, cinema, mixed gatherings, bars, cafes or pubs, alcohol – anything Western is proscribed.

Joy is muted and frowned on. Except for rejoicing in Allah.

Social contact between the sexes before marriage is sinful. Even having a coffee or a lemonade with someone of the opposite sex – don't even try it.

Islam is obsessed with sex and its repression. Muslim women claim 'The Veil' is their choice of attire.

Far from being merely clothing – or as is claimed 'Tradition' - the burqa shows a meek subservience to the males in their society, husbands, fathers, brothers… A visible acceptance of a woman's inferior status and her total obedience to her male 'protectors'.

It denotes to the world the wearer's religion and blazons her piety.

Read on…

In 2017.

A quote from the leading Muslim authority in Great Britain: **Tariq Ramadan, Professor of Contemporary Islamic Studies, Oxford University, a post he has held for eighteen years – since 2009.**

"Either you wear the veil or you get raped." Ramadan has been suspended from his teaching position in Oxford. Three accusations of rape against him in the UK and two more in France – including death threats and extreme physical violence towards his victims –

are being investigated. According to Ramadan, if his victims were unveiled they were asking for it.

A Sharia court would acquit him. At a meeting I attended at the Royal Geographical Society (of which I am a Fellow) Ramadan held up his British Passport. After eighteen years occupying his chair at Oxford University, with all the privileges and rights of living in our humane and well-ordered society and the freedoms of a way of life unimaginable in any Muslim Theocracy, he affirmed ,

"This is a Travel Document. My only loyalty is to Islam." There were raucous shouts of approval from a row of black tents behind me. He is a charismatic man of perhaps fifty with an adoring female following.

Islamists today have mined an ancient text which is to say the least ambiguous, to extrapolate a manifesto for A Death Cult.

I have read The Qu'ran. In translation of course – which Muslims will say does not count. Like all ancient works of literature, written when few could read, it was intended to be spoken. The *Epic of Gilgamesh*, Homer, Virgil, Dante, Beowulf, the Vegas, *the Ramayana, the Mahabharata*, the Bible, the Torah, the Sayings of Siddhartha Gautama, The Buddha, the *Analects of Confucius, The Song of Roland, The Canterbury Tales*- all written to be read aloud. Translations may never have the music, or the inspiring resonance of ancient texts in their original language, but since these texts claim to be universal, their meaning will shine through in other languages. My benchmark is Shakespeare – written specifically to be performed.

I was the Director of The London Shakespeare Group. For sixteen years – for two months every year we travelled the world. Irving Wardle, the Theatre Critic in The Sunday Times wrote – "The London Shakespeare Group must be our most World-Famous company of Actors."

In Beijing we were doing *Twelfth Night* in a vast theatre for the Beijing Opera, and three thousand people were turned away because there were no tickets left.

I have seen three African *Macbeths*. In Xhosa, Swahili and Zulu. The Russians have filmed a towering *Hamlet*. The Japanese have made several Shakespeare based films, *Throne of Blood* from *Macbeth*, *Ran* from *King Lear*. His 37 plays have been translated into every known language, including Mandarin, Welsh, Yoruba, and are still being performed all over the world.

Too many operas in too many languages to be quoted here.

While despising all signs of joy in unbelievers, young Muslims are consumed by envy of the Western way of life. It is understandable that they feel such violent hatred towards Western culture, as they cannot avoid seeing in the streets and on television the freedom and the guilt-free happiness experienced by heterogeneous youngsters in the West, of all religions or none – a freedom and a joy they are forbidden to share because they are Muslims. So they strap themselves into high explosives or drive a ten-ton truck into a carefree crowd of holidaymakers in a seaside resort, including toddlers and young children, and turn the rejoicing throng into an *abattoir*.

I have lived and worked in a great many Muslim countries. Syria, Egypt, Morocco, Tunisia, Iraq. Four of the Seven Emirates: Bahrain, Abu Dhabi, Dubai, Sharjah. Also: Oman, Jordan, Nigeria, Indonesia, Malaysia, Pakistan, including six weeks in Saudi Arabia.

All because of Shakespeare. Crossing the border from the ravishing technicolour bedlam that is India into the gloom of Pakistan speaks volumes.

I make friends easily, but friendship with 'Infidels' is strongly discouraged in the Instruction Manual which is The Qu'ran. I affirm that many of the Muslim men I met in my travels were decent, often charming and friendly to me, an Infidel, although in conversation we kept well away from science, philosophy and religion. I got no impression at all of women inside their tents, which is a testament to the tents' efficacy in making their wearers invisible, and children crept closer to their mothers' silhouettes at the sight of unbelievers.

Without a father who took a long time to die due to wounds in the First World War, I was brought up entirely by women – my mother, two older sisters, and a maiden aunt, all of whom I loved immoderately. To this day I am more comfortable in women's company than in men's, and I find societies without women quite alien.

We often perform in out-of-the-way places where, the Ambassador or the Consul will throw a small party after the first night to introduce some of the local people who might help us make the most of our visit.

On our first night in Saudi Arabia I was introduced to a personable young Englishman whom I guessed would be in the Diplomatic Service.

"What do you do?" I asked him, just to make sure. "I'm a male prostitute," he answered without hesitation. Since the likelihood of this statement being true was zero, I understood it was a joke, but couldn't work out the *double-entendre*, so I played along.

I said "Business brisk in Riyadh, I imagine, with most of the talent under wraps."

His laugh confirmed that I had guessed correctly. He was an Under-Secretary at the Embassy.

Then he explained.

"All we Brits in Saudi are here for the money," he said. "No matter what position we hold, and how close we are to the King and The Court, we are all being lavishly paid so we keep quiet and shut our eyes and ears to politics…

"And we feel bad about ourselves. But not bad enough, obviously, or we wouldn't still be here. So calling ourselves 'prostitutes' is defensive hypocrisy. We say it before you do." Later, at a gathering including many expat Brits, I was asked if I should like to accompany them to a sports arena at the weekend, where we could witness amputations of the hands of felons, which attract enthusiastic crowds, or beheadings of dissidents out of favour with the House of Saud. I refused of course.

But not before considering their offer. I was young, keen to experience everything, planning to be a writer. I would not be causing the butchery, was incapable of stopping it even if I had the courage of a lion. I would be a witness, nothing more. And nobody need know unless I told them.

I hesitated. What would my family and friends say? What would they think of me? Would I ever sleep again? I freely admit to being lily-livered. During six months filming in Spain, for *El Cid*, I saw many bullfights.

I was angry – even distraught at the cruel spectacle. But from my own experience I have found that pain is not felt during trauma; shock is an anaesthetic and pain starts only in tranquillity.

I had an accident in my car in Italy. I fractured a thorassic vertebra and broke several ribs. No one else was involved. It was not till I was rescued that the pain took me by the throat and I begged for painkillers. There are other reasons, however, for deploring the hideous cruelty of bull- fighting. Although Matadors are not infrequently killed, and more often badly gored, the *Corrida* is not an equal contest. The audience is seated all round the arena and well out of danger. The bulls are kept in stalls in utter darkness up until the moment they are goaded towards the narrow passage leading to a heavy wooden door which opens onto the *Plaza di Toros*. While they are penned in this passage, the Picadors stab the animal with their *Pic*s, jagged darts streaming with bright ribbons which lodge in the bull's flesh, maddening the animal before the gate thunders open and he charges blinded into the blazing afternoon. Two more *Toreros* wave their magenta capes to get the bull's attention, taunting him while the *Matador,* who is "The Hero" of this Drama takes up his stance opposite his adversary. The *Matador* now shows off his courage. Time after time, he lures the frenzied animal closer and closer to his tight satin crotch, catching the horns in his cape at the very last moment.   The audience gasps…The *Matador* is now taunting the bull on his knees, the vicious sweep of the weary bull's horns missing the Torero's head by a centimetre. The bullfighter makes several passes with his cape, risking death with each fresh charge. Flaunting his courage and his dexterity at avoiding the curve of the lethal horns he brandishes his dazzling skill.   The flaming red lining of the cape looks to the bull like the body of his elusive torturer. The bull charges time after time, until, weakened by the wounds inflicted by the jagged darts still embedded in his flesh, blood pouring from his nose and from his eyes, cascading down his black glistening flanks, and half dead with exhaustion, he sinks to his knees. Simultaneously the Hero rises to his feet. The *Matador* is standing now.

He raises his sword and aiming the point of it through the horns of the magnificent beast, with a last balletic flourish, he plunges the weapon up to the hilt between the dying bull's blood-soaked shoulders. Almost in slow motion the animal's muscles contract briefly, his hide flutters like a distant echo of thunder, before he sinks apologetically to the arena floor, raising puffs of wind-blown sand as a torrent of blood pours from his throat.

The crowded terraces erupt with post coital rapture. "Ole" "OLE!" they shout. The *Matador,* bows humbly, to renewed cheering. *Il Presidente* hacks an ear from the bloody corpse, the trophy awarded for a magnificent duel, and he presents it to the *Matador* who accepts it while bowing and showing off his prize to the howling terraces. I saw many *Corridas*. They are a celebrated Spanish tradition. However much I protest at the cruelty, the roar of the crowd is intoxicating, the spectacle is unbearably tragic and deeply disturbing and the greatest Matadors like Manolete have the grace of Nureyev, the courage of Hercules and the mythic beauty of Theseus despatching the Minotaur.

I was young, bowled over by the strangeness, carried away by the excitement, with no wish to sour the pleasure of our Spanish hosts.

So I feigned rapture and hid my hypocrisy till I was back in my apartment

***

What is needed is not the will to believe but the will to find out which is its exact opposite.
Bertrand Russell.

Doubt is not a pleasant condition, but certainty is absurd.
Voltaire.

Islam teaches that infidels follow the laws of man, but that Muslims follow the laws of God. No Muslim would presume to know the mind of God. He must rely on the Imams' interpretation of the word of God in the Qu'ran. And being an ancient opaque and complex text the meaning is not always readily understood. The Imams deliver translations that are approved by Qu'ranic Scholars, so devout Muslims are therefore puppets of the priests.

'Scholars' in Muslem lands are not polymaths as we expect a 'scholar' to be in the West. 'Islamic Scholar's' field of study is so narrow, the definition 'scholar' is a misnomer. They should be called 'Qu'ranic Interpreters'. Along with the sayings of Mohammed and Sharia Law the only text they study is the Qu'ran – transcribed by camel-herders nearly two thousand years ago. Mohammed claims that this text was revealed to him by the Angel Gabriel while the Prophet was meditating in a cave. Some of the passages are lifted from the Old Testament and the Torah – Jesus is considered to be an important precursor to Mohammed and the fact that The Prophet could neither read nor write has not hindered Muslims from believing that every word of the Qu'ran issued from the mouth of Allah – with supernatural vocal chords, obviously. Perhaps the Angel Gabriel was a ventriloquist.

All religions begin with a fairy tale. Stories of real life are too mundane to inspire sufficient awe. Scientology is gibberish, invented by a science-fiction author, L. Ron Hubbard in the forties, to make money. The world is full of suckers, and he succeeded. Christians believe that Mary the mother of Jesus was Immaculate, and that her husband Joseph, was not the father of Jesus because God was. At Holy Communion, the Sacrament, consisting of a wafer and a sip of wine, is administered by the priest. Wars have been fought over the question of whether the wafer and the wine are *symbols* of the flesh and blood of Jesus, or whether the Priest by Holy Magic turns these items into the real thing and his communicants into cannibals. To question the Qu'ran is punishable by Death.

We question to find out. How else do we learn?

J.F.

Death

The favourite Islamic penalty for transgressions. There is no shortage of volunteers for decapitating any who have offended Allah. A few weeks ago I read in the Times, that in Pakistan, a family were at prayer, when a fourteen year-old girl accidentally tore a page of the Qu'ran. Her father instantly beheaded his own daughter. Paradise and its amenities is not on offer to apostates after they are dead. Even comic books – *Charlie Hebdo* in Paris – along with any text at all that is not orthodox Islamic, is *haram*.

There were more books translated into Spanish last year, than have been translated into Arabic since the tenth century.

All human knowledge is contained in books. In the Golden Age of Islam, books were treasured and their contents revered. Now IslamISM forbids Muslims from reading Western writing. The seventh century Qu'ran is the only book they know. In the twenty-first century, how can wisdom be pursued under these constraints?

Jesus was a carpenter whose message is love and forgiveness. He wouldn't hurt a fly. Buddha teaches the sanctity of life and non-violence. Meditation and inner peace and kindness to all living things are the Buddha's messages. Flies were safe with him too. The ferocity of Mohammed's hatred of infidels is the inspiration for today's Jihadists burning for revenge as they see it – for the Crusades, for Afghanistan, for Iraq, for Palestine, for being Unbelievers. He started his young adult life as a merchant but he soon found his calling as a perfect role model for today's *Jihadists*. He was a warrior.

In the biography of Mohammed – the *Sira* – it is written that the prophet *personally* beheaded over eight hundred men and boys from a Jewish tribe – the Banu Qurayza – a bloodbath which is refuted by some Muslims today in the face of incontrovertible evidence. Millions of boy babies born to Muslim parents are called "Mohammed" because The Prophet is their ideal role model. It isn't a name. It is an *"Essential Epithet"* - a description, or an adjective, and it means "The Immaculate" or "The Sacred." Like *Christ* for Jesus. Jesus is a common boy's name in Spain. Nowhere are boys called "Christ". Five hundred years before "Mohammed" was born, although the Israelites spoke Aramaic, Jesus was called "Mohammed." In 'The Book', Allah is invoked as 'The Merciful'. 'The Book' exposes this description as wishful thinking.

In Muslim countries, women are invisible beneath the veil, and absent from gatherings. Men alone do not make a civilised society. When massed together men's testosterone transforms them into a mob – viz. football stadia. Women and particularly children have to be protected, and their presence in a crowd deters murderous violence.

No Islamic theocracy acknowledges the greatest scientific discovery since time began, 'Darwin's Theory of Evolution' that explains the miracle of human development and all life on earth.

Nor such Western Poison as The Enlightenment, or **The Age of Reason.**

Jesus's message is love and forgiveness. Buddha teaches the sanctity of life and non-violence. Mohammed urges peace for Muslims, but Death for everyone else.

There are no Catholic, Quaker, Jewish, Hindu, Buddhist or Atheist suicide bombers.

When the refugee crisis was at its peak, the richest Kingdom in Arabia made an offer. The largest Arab state after Algeria, Saudi Arabia, consists of 2.5 million square miles of sand.

Israel has made the desert bloom. Their engineers have built vast machines which desalinate thousands of gallons of seawater into sweet drinkable water at an affordable cost. Saudi Arabia could do the same and irrigate the desert. The refugee crisis would be over. There is also a recent, miraculous scientific discovery called 'Graphene'. It is a substance light as a spider's web and stronger than steel. It could be made into a mesh so strong and yet so fine, it could desalinate the ocean.

With their countless billions of dollars… what was the Saudi offer?

To build a hundred mosques in Germany the preferred destination for many desperate Muslims. <u>A Hundred Mosques.</u>

For thousands of starving, terrified refugees, seeking safety from their fellow Muslims, and a home to lay their exhausted children down to sleep.

In plainer words. The Saudis want to secure a beach- head for Islam in the largest and richest country in Europe.

Islam is a proselytising religion. Its oft vaunted aim is to Islamicise the world. The refugees are fleeing for their lives, from war, starvation, from bombs and bullets, from murderous violence, from the perpetual brutal Civil War in Syria, from conflicts between one Muslim believer and another, Shia against Sunni, Saudi Arabia and Iran, Daesh and Isis and The Islamic State. In their rejection of fellow religionists, they are also fleeing the horrors of Islam*ism*.

The Saudis kill journalists who publish the truth, like Jamal Kashoggi. They hoped that the vigilant world press waiting outside the Embassy in Istanbul where his murder took place wouldn't notice the smell from the bulging luggage (containing his chopped- up corpse) as it was packed into the SUV parked outside. They didn't succeed with the last bit. Kashoggi's murder and dismemberment made headlines all over the western world.

The only gentle and tolerant version of Islam, the Sufis are abhorred by other Muslims because they play music and drums, they recite poetry, and dance. They are happy! And they welcome fellow humans to their celebrations, regardless of their religion or their race. Among all the Islamic countries, only Jordan has opened its arms to thousands of refugees. But hundreds more reject sanctuary with their co-

religionists. They want to come to Europe, to the lands of the Infidels. And many of them drown or die in the attempt.

A third of the population of Saudi Arabia is made up of indentured labourers from Pakistan and the Philippines – the workhorses that power the egregious luxury of the House of Saud, with its fleet of private jets and glossy limousines. In Islam, no mixing of the sexes is permitted – unless the couples are married.

The young sheiks work off their monumental frustrations behind the wheel. In the dusk before the evening meal, when young Italians parade up and down the main thoroughfares of their towns in *La Passeggiata* gossiping and flirting decorously, the young Saudis roar up and down the motorways in their fabulous Maserati's and Ferrari's at lunatic speeds. Accidents are part of the fun since money is no object.

Roundabouts have been renamed - 'Straight-On-Abouts'.

The workers from Pakistan are all Muslims. Their passports – along with the Filippinos', who are Christians (i.e. Infidels) are commandeered on arrival, which effectively turns the workers into captives.

There are seven million of these workers. They are housed in over-crowded dormitories like battery hens and they work and are treated as slaves, like the *Dalit* – the untouchables – in India. Despite war and famine, it is now clear that this tumultuous exodus of refugees is also a flight from the strictures of Islam**ism**. Yet there is a dreadful contradiction in their plight. Youngsters see how the West lives on their television sets and their iPhones, and they want it. They want all the advantages of Western democracy, while their brainwashing from an early age ensures that they cannot countenance a life without the certainties of their Faith. Safe in their new destinations, they demand Mosques and Sharia Law, *halal* butchers and females imprisoned and rightless in *purdah*. They want segregated schools for children, and Islamic curricula, waving us all on to a Hellish Sharia future with women enslaved with no legal rights, confined to their homes, genital mutilation (pre-Islamic, but still practiced in many Muslim countries, and also in Great Britain by 'Tradition'-fixated Muslim women), homosexuals thrown from high buildings, honour killings, intersexual friendships forbidden, and beheadings, stonings, and amputations their only entertainment.

The closure of public swimming pools for women-only days. They want, in other words, to have their cake and eat it. They want to hijack our democracy (which is far from perfect, but light years ahead of any of the Islamic Theocracies I have encountered) and Islamicise us at the catastrophic expense of our Western way of life. The overall population of Muslims in the UK is only 5% – though in London it is four times that. We didn't invite them here yet they demand all these privileges as their right.

In the UK, a pusillanimous reluctance to breathe a word against Islam for fear of being accused of Islamophobia is tricking us into a horrifying Sharia future. A 'phobia, (I quote from The New Oxford English Dictionary,) is "an

irrational or an exaggerated fear of something."

I don't call fear of planes flying into skyscrapers leaving three thousand dead, fear for our children being slaughtered at a pop concert, toddlers being dismembered by suicide bombers or ten-ton trucks in a holiday resort 'irrational' or 'exaggerated'. I am not ashamed to call myself anti-

Islam as it is practised today by *Jihadists*

"Islamophobia" suggests something disproportionate, racist, and immoral. None of which applies to me. It is not Muslims I deplore, but the ideology

of extremism… if Muslims could recapture the wisdom and the tolerance the creativity, and humanity of their Golden Age, the world would be a finer, kinder place.   If Islam is the centre of your life, and most Muslims claim that it is, UK

Citizens must unite to stop you from destroying our flawed but wonderful democracy, hard-fought-for over hundreds of years.

Go to an Islamic country, where Muslims aren't killing each other – if you can find one. **Or go to Saudi Arabia, the birthplace and the beating heart of your Faith.**

Make the Saudis welcome you, and make the desert bloom for you, their brothers. How can anyone forget the television coverage of the tragic thousands, adults and children, tramping through an alien world, in search of a refuge? Or the overloaded dinghies, spilling their desperate cargoes into the sea to drown? But if you were born in England, or wish to stay here – **you** must adapt **to us**. Political IslamISM is incompatible with our life in the West.

The Qu'ran -this Ancient Instruction manual for - - **SEVENTH CENTURY MUSLIMS-** must be revised to accommodate the Human Rights which have evolved in civilised societies since AD 610.

For the many thousands of Muslims who have arrived here or were born here you can worship as you wish in any of the 1,750 Mosques built in our tolerant, multi-faith country. In the street your women's religious garb is provocative in a secular society, suggesting that to be heavily veiled displays virtue, and visually shouting "apartness" in defiance of our cohesive, multi-cultural democracy. According to Tariq Ramadan, our women, in their shameless jeans and revealing jumpers, with their hair tumbling about their painted faces are "begging to be raped." New arrivals must assimilate and in no circumstances should men or women command respect for their religious choices. For multiple reasons – **THE FACE VEIL MUST BE BANNED.** In a society that aspires to equality we cannot allow a minority to shut out the rest of the world as if godlessness were infectious like cholera. We are profoundly insulted. The Yashmak is a Persian invention, predating Islam by more than a hundred and fifty years. It is Zoroastrian, and thus Pagan in origin.

It is never mentioned in the Qu'ran. Neither is the Burqa. The Qu'ran suggests that women should dress modestly, that is all. The Yashmak showed that the woman who wore it was the property of her husband or her Master and that she was his **SLAVE**. Feminists must add their voices to the protest.

Schooling

It is impossible to teach or to learn if either teacher or pupil is wrapped up like a parcel.

The Law

Police stations, supermarkets, shop lifting, street crime, law courts, identity parades, shopping malls and markets, public transport.

DAILY LIFE! FRIENDLY COMMUNITIES!

Do Muslims have to demonstrate their piety and their aloofness from the irreligious societies they have chosen to invade? Now you are here, you may worship as you please, but your acceptance of our way of life outside your Mosques is non-negotiable. It is a fee that you must pay for the incalculable advantages of living in our civilised society. Refugees have chosen to seek asylum in Infidel countries. They constantly affirm they can't wait to see the Crescent Moon Flag flying over our Houses of Parliament. In Saudi Arabia the Wahabi Religious Police wield whips, with which they lash any woman's flesh if they catch a glimpse of it – where hair escapes from a headscarf, or on her ankles above her shoes.

In every publication, including newspapers and periodicals, photographs of Western women, with their hair uncovered, or their clothing deemed to be immodest, are excised by scissors, as are any texts considered subversive to Islam. Newspapers are frequently more holes than copy. Muslim's refuse to befriend us – **by Allah's instructions in the Q'ran**.

Their insistence on separate seating for males and females… Apart from the fanatics continually trying to murder us, even spineless vegetables (to mix a metaphor) can hardly be expected to clasp such hostile strangers to our bosoms. The mummifying of all your females – including some five- and six-year-old girls I have seen smothered from head to toe in black bombazine - is an indictment of your sex-obsessed paranoia posing as 'Tradition'. The seventh century was a very long time ago, and Mohammed never specified covering the face and every inch of flesh, let alone on children. Ed Husain and Majid Nawaz of the Quilliam Foundation, both loyal Muslims, are heroically trying to combat Extremism. I am not optimistic that they will succeed in persuading Muslims to cohabit in peace with Infidels. Countless Islamist terrorist outrages are thwarted <u>daily</u> by our brilliant security services.

Our police force was formed to protect law-abiding citizens from criminals, and to preserve the peace without repression in a well-ordered society. Not to fight a guerrilla war against fanatical ideologues who are seriously intent on killing us and dying in rapture in the name of Allah. Anjim Choudary, A Hate Preacher soon to be released from Belmarsh prison boasted: **"In the West you are in love with Life. We Muslims are in love with Death."** Every sect wants to kill all other sects. Except the loathed and gentle Sufis, with their whirling dervishes, music and poetry and their humanist tolerance of all comers. They seem closer to my conception of what a religion ought to be, than all the other variations of Islam I have encountered. If you doubt Muslims' hostility to non-Muslims in London in 2019 try taking off your shoes and entering a Mosque to have a respectful look around as I did in Regent's Park. Once. You don't half know when you're not welcome. The West is the Future. **Seventh Century Rules no longer apply.** Unlike Mohammed's armies in the seventh century, we will not behead you if you do not convert to Christianity or to secularity. But Muslims **choosing** to live in the West **must** adapt to our Western way of life.

And the West will continue to respect our differences, so long as you stop trying to convert us.

Or to murder our children.

***

By the same Author

Plays

About the Author

John Fraser has made over twenty-five international films and was nominated for a British Academy Award for Best Actor for his role in *The Trials of Oscar Wilde* alongside Peter Finch and James Mason.

He was in *El Cid* with Charlton Heston and Sophia Loren, *Repulsion* opposite Catherine Deneuve (directed by Roman Polanski) and *Isadora* opposite Vanessa Redgrave. In 1980 John founded The London Shakespeare Group with which he has travelled all over the world.

He lived for forty years in Tuscany.

He now lives in London.

Close Up

The wittiest and best written show-business autobiography I have ever read.
Roger Lewis, *The Sunday Express*

WOODHOUSIAN in its humour.
Jonathan Cecil, *The Spectator*

ONE OF THE YEAR'S MOST ENTERTAINING BOOKS
The Sunday Times

The World is my country, all mankind are my brethren, and to do good is my religion.
Thomas Paine

CPSIA information can be obtained
at www.ICGtesting.com
Printed in the USA
LVHW091517271219
641883LV00002B/266/P

9 781527 254985